101
BIGGEST
MISTAKES

3RD YEAR MEDICAL
STUDENTS MAKE

AND HOW TO
AVOID THEM

101 BIGGEST MISTAKES
3RD YEAR MEDICAL STUDENTS MAKE

AND HOW TO AVOID THEM

SAMIR P. DESAI, MD

Assistant Professor of Medicine, Baylor College of Medicine

Staff Physician, Veterans Affairs Medical Center
Houston Texas

PUBLISHED BY

HOUSTON, TEXAS

P.O. Box 300988
Houston, Texas 77230-0988
(713) 927-6830
www.MD2B.net

The 101 Biggest Mistakes 3*rd* Year Medical Students Make and How to Avoid Them is published by MD2B, P.O. Box 300988, Houston, Texas 77230-0988
http://www.MD2B.net

NOTICE: The author and publisher disclaim any personal liability, either directly or indirectly, for advice or information presented within. The author and publisher have used care and diligence in the preparation of this book. Every effort has been made to ensure the accuracy and completeness of information contained in this book. The reader should understand, however, that the subject matter of the book is not rooted in scientific observation. The recommendations within this book have come from the author's personal experience and interactions with other attending physicians and residents over many years. Since expectations vary from medical school to medical school, clerkship to clerkship, attending physician to attending physician, and resident to resident, the recommendations are not universally applicable. No responsibility is assumed for errors, inaccuracies, omissions, or any false or misleading implication that may arise due to the text.

Printed in the United States of America
ISBN # 0-9725561-0-9

About the Author

Dr. Samir Desai serves on the faculty of the Baylor College of Medicine in the Department of Medicine. Dr. Desai has educated and mentored both medical students and residents, work for which he has received teaching awards.

Dr. Desai conceived and authored the Clinician's Guide Series, a series of books dedicated to providing clinicians with practical approaches to commonly encountered problems. Now in its second edition, the initial book in this series, the Clinician's Guide to Laboratory Medicine, has become a popular book for third year medical students, providing a step-by-step approach to laboratory test interpretation. More recent titles in this series include the Clinician's Guide to Diagnosis and Clinician's Guide to Internal Medicine.

Dr. Desai is also the founder of http://www.MD2B.net, a website committed to helping today's medical student become tomorrow's doctor. Founded in 2002, http://www.MD2B.net is dedicated to providing medical students with the tools needed to tackle the challenges of the clinical years of medical school.

After completing his residency training in Internal Medicine at Northwestern University in Chicago, Illinois, Dr. Desai had the opportunity of serving as chief medical resident. He received his MD degree from the Wayne State University School of Medicine in Detroit, Michigan, graduating first in his class.

Books by Samir Desai, MD

Clinician's Guide to Laboratory Medicine

Clinician's Guide to Diagnosis

Clinician's Guide to Internal Medicine

101 Biggest Mistakes 3rd Year Medical Students Make

To view sample chapters from these books, please visit http://www.MD2B.net

How to Contact the Author

Dr. Samir Desai provides consulting services for third and fourth year medical students. He has given talks about the pitfalls of the third year of medical school, steps to success during clinical clerkships, laboratory test interpretation made easy for the USMLE, applying for residency, and other topics of interest to medical students. Requests for information about consulting services, as well as inquiries about his availability for speeches and seminars, should be directed to the following address:

MD2B
P.O. Box 300988 Houston, Texas 77230-0988
(713) 927-6830

Readers of this book are also encouraged to contact the author with comments and ideas for future editions of this book (email address samir.desai@MD2B.net).

About http://www.MD2B.net

http://www.MD2B.net is a website committed to helping today's medical student become tomorrow's doctor. Founded in 2002, http://www.MD2B.net is dedicated to providing third and fourth year medical students with the tools needed to tackle the challenges of the clinical years of medical school.

The website provides the following information, which complements the content of this book:

Introduction to the 3rd year of medical school
Rotation-specific advice (Internal Medicine, Pediatrics, Surgery, Obstetrics/gynecology, Neurology, Psychiatry)
Do's and Don'ts of the 3rd year of medical school
How to write admit notes
How to write progress notes
How to present patients
How to interpret EKGs
How to interpret chest x-rays

—AND MUCH MORE

Contents

Part IV: *Commonly Made Mistakes* **Throughout the Rotation**

Part V: *Commonly Made Mistakes* **With Residents and Interns**

Part VI: *Commonly Made Mistakes* **During Attending Rounds**

Part VII: *Commonly Made Mistakes* **When Presenting Newly Admitted Patients**

Part VIII: *Commonly Made Mistakes* On Write-Ups

Part IX: *Commonly Made Mistakes* When Giving a Talk

Preface

The third year of medical school is a difficult one. No other year subjects medical students to the gamut of emotions that is experienced during this year. Although exciting, it can also be challenging, frustrating, and anxiety-provoking.

For most students, the third year of medical school is their first time out of the lecture hall. It's like starting a new job. And along with this new job are longer hours, lightning-quick pace, and new work responsibilities. Add to this the fact that third year clerkship grades carry the most weight when it comes time for residency programs to rank their applicants.

Adding to the stress is the fact that medical schools do a relatively poor job of helping students transition between the second and third years of medical school. The time spent in clinical activities during the basic science years is limited (i.e., physical diagnosis course) and is not representative of what life is really like during clinical rotations.

Not only does this affect the performance of students at the start of the year but it also impacts their performance with the start of every new rotation. Too often, students are left on their own to figure out just what it takes to do well on the rotation. By the time they learn the tricks of the trade, it's time to move on to a different rotation.

Every year, however, there are medical students who consistently perform at a high level during their clinical clerkships. What is it about these students that set them apart from their colleagues? Do they do better because they are smarter? In my opinion, it's not simply about smarts. I argue that the major difference between students who do well and students who are average performers is that the former are savvy.

What do I mean by this? Savvy students not only work hard, they know what it takes to impress attending physicians and residents. They learn these skills early in the rotation, giving them an edge.

The purpose of this book is to help third year medical students become savvy. This book achieves its goals by discussing the biggest mistakes students make. It also provides insight into what attending physicians are looking for in their students.

It is my hope that this book will empower you, placing you in a position to have a successful experience, no matter what rotation or clerkship you are on. After all, the expectations of those that are evaluating you are remarkably similar, irrespective of the rotation. Once you are aware of the mistakes third year medical students make, you can do everything in your power to avoid them, thereby becoming the savvy student that is poised for clerkship success.

Having said this, it is important not to lose track of what's important during the third year of medical school, which is to provide excellent patient care while developing the skills to become a competent physician. It is the intent of this book to demystify the third-year experience so that less time is spent trying to figure out how to do well in the rotation, thereby allowing more time to spend on acquiring the skills to be an excellent physician.

Samir Desai, MD

Part I

Commonly Made Mistakes

Before the Rotation Starts

The steps you take before your rotation ever starts are crucial to your success. During the third year, you often have no more than a weekend between the end of one rotation and the start of another. It's only natural to put off thinking about your next rotation until this weekend in between, given the fact that your current rotation is likely to take up much of your time. But the savvy medical student realizes that a little bit of preparation can go a long way in terms of getting you off to a good start. In this chapter, we will discuss mistakes students make before the rotation starts.

Mistake # 1

Not getting the 'nitty-gritty' about the rotation from other medical students

Before you start any rotation, you need to do your homework. This means calling up classmates who have already gone through the rotation. After talking with them, you will have a better idea of what to expect and what you need to do in order to do well in the rotation.

Success tip # 1

Find out as much as you can about the rotation from classmates who have already completed the rotation. You should also speak to a few upper-levels so you can get their thoughts on how to do well.

Talk to as many people as you can. You definitely need the answers to the following questions:

- How will you be evaluated?

- Who will be evaluating you?

- What are the must-have books?

- What is the exam format?

These answers and other information you learn through networking can be invaluable.

Also contact upper levels at your school for their insight, especially if the rotation that you are doing is the first one of the year. Keep in mind, though, that this information may not be current.

Mistake # 2

Getting on the wrong team

Several weeks to a month before your rotation starts, find out which attending physicians and residents will be on service during your rotation. Once you have this knowledge, talk to your classmates or students in the class above you to find out which of the attending physicians and residents are excellent teachers. Your goal is to be placed on their team. Typically, it is a secretary in the department who assigns students to the various teams. At times, however, it may be the chief resident.

Although some programs are receptive to your requests, others have a policy not to accept them. If this is the case, I am afraid that you are out of luck and you will just have to keep your fingers crossed. If they do honor these requests, make sure you call early enough to arrange this. Obviously, you want to call before team assignments are created. Also, keep in mind that your fellow students may have the same idea in mind so it behooves you to try to beat them to the punch.

*Mistake # **3***

Time off is not requested early

The time off that you will have during your third year of medical school will depend upon the rotation. If you should need more time off—maybe your sister is getting married and you need the whole weekend, or you need to go to a conference to present your research—remember to ask for this early in the rotation. In fact, you should bring this to the attention of the course director before the rotation starts so you can be placed on the appropriate team.

If you are given approval for time off by the course director, make sure that you inform your attending physician, resident, and intern that you will be away. I recall one student who was given permission to attend a conference to present some of his research. He informed his resident and intern but failed to inform me, his attending physician, that he would be away for four days. Needless to say, I was not impressed with his professionalism.

Remember that you are part of a team. The team functions best when all of its members are present. So if you need to be away, recognize that someone else will have to pick up the slack. Don't forget to thank those that fulfill your responsibilities while you are gone. Before you leave, volunteer to make up the time you will be away.

Mistake # **4**

Not having the equipment to do the job

As with any job, in order to do it well, you need to have the proper equipment. The tools that you need are listed in the following table, according to the rotation.

Rotation	Equipment needed
Internal Medicine	Stethoscope (alcohol wipes to clean off scope's bell) Penlight Reflex hammer Tuning fork Visual acuity card Calculator Ophthalmoscope
Pediatrics	Stethoscope (alcohol wipes to clean off scope's bell) Ophthalmoscope Otoscope (including otoscope tips) Calculator

Ob/Gyn	Stethoscope (alcohol wipes to clean off scope's bell) Penlight Pregnancy wheel Reflex hammer Bandage scissors Tape Gauze
Surgery	Stethoscope (alcohol wipes to clean off scope's bell) Scissors Paper tape Kerlix Cover sponges Penlight
Neurology	Stethoscope (alcohol wipes to clean off scope's bell) Ophthalmoscope Eye chart Tuning fork Penlight

You will, of course, need something to carry all this equipment in. Many students place their equipment in their coat pockets while others prefer to carry it in some type of bag. Make sure that you label your more expensive tools because other people will inevitably borrow your equipment. You certainly do not want your stethoscope or ophthalmoscope to walk away.

Mistake # 5

Not having the books you need

It is better to have the books (printed or electronic) you need in your hands before the rotation starts. Your fellow students will be able to tell you which book is required for the rotation and which books they found useful. After talking with them, you may feel tempted to go on a shopping spree. Before you make the bookstore owner's day, I encourage you to take a close look at the books that have been recommended. If the information in the book is presented in a way that is pleasing to you and fits with the way you process information, then you should consider buying the book, especially if it complements your required course book.

Keep in mind that many of these books are also available in the medical library. So instead of buying the book, you may be able to check it out. If your school library's copy is checked out, try your hospital's library. Another option is to borrow the book.

If you don't purchase the book(s) before your rotation starts, make sure you do so in the first day or two of the rotation. The idea is to arm yourself as soon as possible with the resources you need to excel.

Your intern, resident, and attending physician will also have thoughts on useful books, so make sure you pick their brains as well.

Mistake # <u>6</u>

Forgetting that the clinical evaluation counts much more than the exam

Keep in mind that the grading system during your clinical clerkships is different from that which you have been accustomed to during your basic science years. During the basic science years, your grade was based on objective findings—how well you did on the exam. In your clinical rotations, the bulk of your grade will be based on your clinical evaluation. While most clinical clerkships have exams at the end of the rotation, the weight the exam carries in the overall determination of the grade is considerably less than the clinical evaluation.

Success tip # 2
Although you will still have an exam at the end of the rotation, it counts much less than your clinical evaluation. Don't focus so much on the exam that you let your clinical evaluation suffer.

Part II

Commonly Made Mistakes

Early in the Rotation

The start of a new rotation is always difficult. Since it is an entirely new experience, it's not uncommon to feel ill at ease during the first few days. After all, you won't be familiar with how things work.

In the first few days, lay the groundwork, so to speak, for a successful experience. In other words, you need to become savvy. By savvy, I mean that you need to quickly ascertain the rules, responsibilities, and expectations during this rotation.

In this chapter, we will discuss common mistakes students make early in the rotation. By the time these students do get savvy, it's often too late to impress the superiors because it's time to move on to the next rotation. Here's how you can avoid this.

Mistake # 7

Daydreaming during the clerkship orientation

On the first day of your clerkship, you will have an orientation, typically given by the clerkship director. During the orientation, your clerkship director will convey a lot of information regarding the rotation. It's in your best interests to write this information down. Don't rely on your memory.

> ### Success tip # 3
> Make sure you TAKE NOTES during your clerkship orientation. Since your clerkship director will bombard you with lots and lots of important information, it's in your best interests to write things down. If you don't, you put yourself at risk of forgetting something very important, which can have major consequences for your grade.

Mistake # **8**

Not knowing what needs to be done to get honors

Before or shortly after you start a rotation, you should be familiar with criteria needed for getting honors in the clerkship. Pay close attention to what your clerkship director says during orientation. He or she will often state what needs to be done in order to do well in the rotation. In most clerkships, your clinical performance (as evaluated by your intern, resident, attending physician) carries more weight than your exam score. If at all possible, try to get a look at the evaluation form so you can find out what skills will be evaluated.

> ### Success tip # 4
> Do you know the criteria for getting honors? If not, do not pass go! You are doing a great disservice to yourself. It's useful to take a look at the evaluation form early on in the rotation to know the skills that will be evaluated.

Mistake # **9**

Failing to make the most out of the first day of the rotation

The first day of every rotation is a time to get oriented. On the first day, you should try to accomplish the following:

- Familiarize yourself with the surroundings by walking around the hospital

- Locate the supply room, utility rooms (dirty/clean), staff bathrooms, etc. on the your ward

- Find out how the rooms are numbered

- Find out where the resident lounge is

- Find out where the call room is

- Find out where the library is

- Find out where the cafeteria and vending machines are

- Locate medical records department

- Obtain a hospital telephone directory or make your own phone number list. Include phone numbers for the nurses' stations, x-ray file room, lab, pharmacy, operating room

- Obtain beeper numbers for every member of your team and put it on your phone number list or other easily accessible location

- Get a weekly schedule (ie., conferences and required lectures)

11

- Go over a typical day with the intern and/or resident (ie., what time do work or attending rounds start?)

- Find out what your work responsibilities are

- Find out about the call schedule

- Get familiar with paperwork (ie., forms needed for admit note, progress notes, etc.)

- Get familiar with the computer system

It's important that you accomplish all of the above on the first day. As you set about trying to do so, you should realize that you will be bombarded with a lot of information on the first day of a new rotation. That's why it's important to write things down. The idea is to learn as much as you can about how things work as soon as possible so that you can put yourself in a position to do your best work.

Success tip # 5

You can't possibly do your best work if you are not comfortable with your surroundings. The only way to get comfortable is to accomplish all of the above as soon as possible. Remember the goal is to get savvy quickly because the savvy student is the one who does well.

Mistake # **10**

Not meeting with the attending physician early in the rotation

Meeting with the attending physician early in the rotation is an absolute must. This meeting will help you open up the lines of communication. After this meeting, you will have a good feel for what your attending physician expects from you during your rotation.

If you don't have this meeting, what inevitably happens is that an air of uncertainty will hang over your head. For example, if you don't ask your attending about how he or she prefers you to present your patients during rounds, you will be corrected during rounds the first time you present. Avoid this, as well as other unpleasant interactions right from the get go.

Success tip # 6

Not meeting with the attending physician in the first few days of a new rotation is a recipe for disaster. You need to know exactly what the attending is expecting of you. Meeting his or her expectations is the KEY to doing well.

Ideally, this meeting should take place on the first day of the rotation. In reality, it may be difficult to do so because of your attending physician's schedule. Try at least to meet sometime over the next few days.

In a perfect world, your attending physician would initiate the meeting. Unfortunately, not all attending physicians recognize the importance of this meeting. If this is so, set it up yourself.

Mistake # 11

Not meeting with the resident early in the rotation

Although the attending physician is the leader of the team, you will be working much more closely with your resident. Because the resident's expectations for you often differ from that of the attending, you need to know what these expectations are.

Success tip # 7

ALWAYS meet with your resident in the first few days of the rotation to go over his or her expectations. These expectations will differ from those of the attending physician. If you meet the resident's expectations, not only will you receive a great evaluation, he or she may also clue you in as to what the attending physician will ask you during attending rounds.

If you do everything you can to meet his or her expectations, the resident will have more interest in teaching you. Remember that the resident will formally evaluate you and therefore have input in the determination of your overall grade. Also, it is not uncommon for attending physicians to inquire about your performance outside of attending rounds. Don't give your resident a reason to speak about you in any way that is not glowing.

Mistake # 12

Not meeting with the intern early in the rotation

Although the attending physician and resident are the leaders of the team, you will be working much more closely with your intern. You should make it a point to meet with your intern early in the rotation. During this meeting, you should strive to find out what your intern expects from you during the rotation. The expectations of the intern often differ from that of the attending and resident. If you do everything you can to meet these expectations, the intern will have more interest in teaching you.

Although the intern may formally evaluate your performance, at some institutions interns do not have a say in the determination of your overall grade. Regardless of whether they have formal input, the attending physician and resident often rely on their input to determine your grade. It behooves you to maintain a solid relationship with your intern so that if asked about your performance, your intern can speak about you in glowing terms.

Mistake # <u>13</u>

Slacking off during the first few days of the rotation

On the first few days of any rotation, it's important that you get off to a good start. The best way to do this is to work hard. This will help you build a good working relationship with your resident and intern. The residents will teach you much more if you are a hard worker. This extra teaching can be invaluable in that residents can often predict what attending physicians may ask during attending rounds. In addition to being a hard worker, you also want to show your team that you are friendly, courteous, and interested.

Success tip # 8
In the first few days of a new clerkship, working hard is the key to getting off to a good start.

Part III

Commonly Made Mistakes

When Admitting Patients

Patients will be assigned to you when your team is admitting. The term admitting refers to the time during which your team is accepting new patients. After your resident assigns you a patient, it is your responsibility to complete an admission work-up on the patient(s) assigned to you.

Regardless of the rotation, the basic work-up includes performing a thorough history and physical exam and obtaining laboratory/diagnostic test results. Once you have gathered all this information, you are ready to sift through all this information in an attempt to explain why the patient has come in with the complaints he or she has. Your job is to establish a diagnosis using the information that you have gathered. Once the diagnosis is established (or you have a presumed diagnosis), you can decide on what further testing is necessary, if any, as well as the treatment plan.

In this chapter, we will discuss common mistakes third year medical students make when admitting patients. These mistakes can be of major consequence since they can lead to mistakes in your oral patient presentation and write-up. Since the people who evaluate you form most of their impression about you on the quality of your oral patient presentations and write-ups (to be discussed in future chapters), it behooves you to avoid these mistakes.

Mistake # <u>14</u>

Not understanding responsibilities when admitting patients

As a third year medical student, you will typically pick up new patients when your team is admitting or on call. Your team is said to be admitting when you are accepting new patients. What typically happens is that the resident will assign one or more patients to you. Once you are assigned a patient, you have a number of responsibilities. These include the following:

- Performing a thorough admission evaluation or work-up

- Performing the necessary scutwork on your patient (see mistake # 36)

- Writing admit orders

- Presenting your patient(s) at attending rounds the next day

Mistake # <u>15</u>

Patient is not seen alone

When you are assigned a patient, you will often have a choice of seeing the patient alone or with the rest of the team. Although both options have merit, I encourage you to opt for the former more than the latter for a variety of reasons:

- First of all, you must perform a thorough history and physical examination while your intern and resident are more interested in a focused history and physical examination. So if you see the patient together, you will often have to come back to the patient's room to fill in the gaps.

- If you do go to see the patient with the intern and resident, what often happens is that they will allow you to start the interview but at some point will take over because they have to operate within time constraints. Remember that while you usually have one patient to work up, they have a number of new patients they need to see and evaluate. So naturally they are pressed for time. Once again, you will have to come back to the patient's room to fill in the gaps.

- At this early point in your career when you are developing your own style and getting comfortable with the history and physical exam-taking process, having your resident and intern next to you may make you nervous or anxious, especially if they start getting uneasy at how long it's taking you to get the history.

For the reasons cited above, I recommend seeing patients assigned to you by yourself more often than not. That's not to say that you should never go to see newly admitted patients with the intern and resident because you should. There's a lot you can learn by watching them perform history and physical examinations.

Mistake # 16

A thorough evaluation of the patient is not performed

Remember that as a medical student, you are expected to perform a thorough patient evaluation. Because you are spending more time with the patient and are following fewer patients, you are expected to know the patient like the back of your hand. This means that every part of the history and physical exam must be done even if you don't think that it is relevant to the issue that brought the patient into the hospital. Thorough patient evaluations performed by medical students have often revealed important information that was not obtained by the intern, resident, or attending physician.

Success tip # 9

Perform thorough history and physical examinations on all newly admitted patients assigned to you. The attending physician expects you to know your patient(s) like the back of your hand.

Mistake # 17

Not meeting with the intern or resident before attending rounds

After you complete your history and physical examination, you need to gather your thoughts regarding your patient. At some point that day, you need to sit down with the intern or resident to go over things. While you are waiting for this meeting to take place, you should look over the information that you have gathered and try to actively process it. Working up a patient is like a solving a puzzle—you have all these pieces of information and you have to see how they fit together. Once you determine this, you will be able to recommend an appropriate treatment plan.

During the problem-solving process, questions that you cannot answer will inevitably arise. That's why you need to sit down with the intern or resident to review the information. Not meeting with the intern or resident can have disastrous consequences in terms of the next day's attending rounds. During attending rounds, your attending will want to know how well you understand your patient and his or her problems. If you have questions that remain unanswered from the admit day, there's a good chance that the attending physician will ask you those very questions.

In order to avoid this situation, you need to meet with the intern or resident on the day that you admit the patient. Don't delay this meeting until the next day because there may not be time.

During your meeting, present the case and your assessment and plan to see if it is in agreement with theirs. This will be good practice for the next day's attending rounds. Your intern and resident can often predict the questions the attending physician will ask you the next day.

Success tip # 10
During attending rounds, your odds of not being able to answer the attending physician's questions skyrocket if you don't go over your patient(s) with the resident or intern.

Mistake # 18

Not having the data you need to write the admit note

Before writing the admit note, you should have all the patient data in front of you. If you don't, you will have to interrupt what you are doing multiple times to search for the information that you need. It will take you much longer to complete a task that already takes quite a while to finish.

The data you need to write the admit note is located in the following:

- Your history and physical exam notes

- ER form

- Old chart/medical records

- Medication list

- Laboratory test results

- EKG interpretation

- Chest x-ray interpretation

- Results of other imaging tests or diagnostic studies

Mistake # 19

Not looking over the old chart

Gaining an understanding of the patient's current illness requires that you know about the patient's past medical history. While some patients can fill you in on their past medical history, there are others who cannot either because they are not good communicators or because they have a problem too complicated for them to explain.

The old chart is one of the best places to find out about the patient's medical history. Many old charts are thick, and at first glance you may wonder how it is possible to sift through all that information. In reality, you can get much of the information you need by reviewing the discharge summaries for each of the patient's past hospitalizations.

Mistake # **20**

Not knowing how to write admit orders

Early in the rotation, you are not expected to be proficient in writing admit orders. With time, however, you should become more comfortable doing so. In general, you should strive to write the admit orders (as well as subsequent daily orders) on every patient you admit. Admit or admission orders are usually written soon after the patient has been evaluated by the team. For more information on writing admit orders, visit www.MD2B.net.

Part IV

Commonly Made Mistakes

Throughout the Rotation

In this chapter we discuss common sense mistakes third year medical students make throughout the rotation. You may be surprised that some of these mistakes are actually made and may say to yourself, "I would never do these things." I feel compelled to share these mistakes with you because I see them repeated time and time again.

Mistake # 21

Being unorganized

I cannot begin to tell you how many times I have asked a medical student for a lab test result only to watch the medical student fumble around, turning over paper after paper in search of the result. In some cases, the student tells me that he or she did not write it down.

I am not alone in having had this experience. Attending physicians understandably get frustrated when medical students do not have data that is clearly pertinent to the patient's hospitalization.

Success tip # 11

Staying organized is a key to rotation success. Strive to be the student who has patient data at your fingertips. Don't be the student who fumbles around, flipping page after page looking for data that your attending physician asks you for.

I always tell my students that organization is half the battle. At times, the amount of information that you gather about your patients can be overwhelming. Take the example of the patient who comes in with diabetic ketoacidosis. A major part of the management of these patients is frequent laboratory testing, sometimes as often as every hour. The only way you can properly manage these patients is to stay organized. You need a system that helps you keep track of the patient's information such as the initial history and physical exam, labs, medications, studies, etc.

I wish I could tell you that one method of staying organized is superior to another, but you need to decide on a system that will work for you. Common methods include the following:

- Clipboard

- Blank or pre-made note cards/sheets

- Pocket-sized notebooks

- Personal digital assistants (PDAs)

There are advantages and disadvantages to each method. Clipboards, for example, are often lost because you have to put them down so many times a day (i.e. when you examine the patient).

Note cards are popular with residents and interns because they are more portable than clipboards. If you do use note cards, remember to include your name and beeper number so that if lost, they may be returned.

In recent times, PDAs have become popular. There are PDA programs that can help you stay on top of things concerning patient care. Regardless of which method you choose to stay organized, have your system in place on day one of the rotation.

Regardless of the method you choose, you should be able to relay the following information within seconds, if asked:

- Patient name

- Medical record or social security number

- Room number

- Date of birth

- Admission date

- Chief complaint

- Brief history of present illness (HPI)

- Results of labs/diagnostic tests

- Medications including frequency, route, and dosage as well as start and end dates

- Daily vital signs and I/O

- Pertinent physical exam findings

- Problem list (patient's active problems) along with management plan

Mistake # **22**

Not getting along with support or ancillary staff

You should make it a point to get along well with not only the team but also with the support staff. The support staff may include nurses, pharmacists, social workers, phlebotomists, as well as other health care professionals.

Although these individuals are usually not part of your team and therefore do not directly evaluate you, they may talk to one of the members of your team, including your attending physician.

Don't give the support staff a reason to talk badly about you. Remember that one of the areas in which you are evaluated is your working relationships. There is no reason why you can't get a stellar evaluation in this area.

Mistake # **23**

Putting your foot in your mouth

Avoid the temptation to say anything negative about your rotation experience, especially remarks about the team members you work with. It's easy to get caught up in these conversations, but remember that the hospital is a very public place and you never know who might be listening. Of course, that's not to say you shouldn't talk about your experiences with others—after all, rotations are stressful and sometimes you just need to vent. Just remember to pick the right time and place to do it. Here's a real-life example:

> Right before beginning his noon lecture, the attending was patiently waiting for the students to grab their food and take a seat before starting the talk on EKG interpretation. Two medical students nearby began talking about their rotation experience.
>
> "So who is your attending this month?" asked Joe.
>
> "I got Dr. Smith. I haven't met him yet because he starts in a few days." replied Sally.

"Oh, you got screwed over. I've heard that he expects you to live, eat, and breathe medicine," responded Joe.

"That figures. I always get stuck with these anal types. There goes my life for the next month," said Sally in exasperation.

Unbeknownst to either student, the attending physician who could hear every word and was about to give the talk was the aforementioned Dr. Smith.

Mistake # 24

Showing up other medical students

This doesn't apply to you if you are the only student on your team. In most cases, though, there will be other students on your team. You have a choice of either working together to help make each other's experience as positive as possible, or you can be at odds with your colleague, with each of you jockeying to outdo the other.

I strongly encourage you to take the former approach. Treat your fellow medical student(s) with respect. Remember that these rotations can be trying at times. Your fellow student is experiencing the same gamut of emotions. So why not band together, offering each other a helping hand and words of encouragement?

If you are at odds with your fellow medical student, believe me, your attending physician will appreciate this tension. That's the last thing you want. After all, most evaluation forms ask your attending to comment on your working relationships with the various team members.

Having said that, I have to recognize that not everything is under your control. If your fellow student wants to be at odds with you, you can't stop him or her. If conflicts arise, it would be wise to meet privately to discuss and, hopefully, resolve the issues.

But whatever you do, don't stoop to his or her level because it will reflect poorly on you. Remember to take the high road—that way, it'll just be your fellow student who gets dinged for his or her inability to get along with others.

Mistake # <u>25</u>

Not notifying the entire team when sick

Everyone gets sick at one time or another. This includes medical students. And sometimes, medical students get sick during rotations. Not uncommonly, students get the mistaken impression that they should not be or are not allowed to be sick. Many times, students just go to work despite feeling less than 100 percent because the illness is not major and it doesn't interfere with their ability to do their job well. But if you are really sick and need to stay at home, it's okay.

When you get sick, the most important thing to do is to take care of yourself. That way you can get better as soon as possible and return to the team as a productive team member. By taking time off to get over your sickness, you also avoid transmitting your illness to patients.

If you do get sick, make sure you call your intern, resident, and attending physician as soon as possible to let them know that you won't be able to come in to work. Also give them some idea of when you think you will be back.

Mistake # <u>26</u>

Dressing unprofessionally

Your attire does matter. What you wear says a lot about you to your colleagues, residents, attending physician, and patients. Always try to dress neatly.

Can I wear scrubs?

> This will vary depending upon your rotation. On your surgical rotation, students are often allowed to wear scrubs all day. You may, however, have to dress professionally when you are seeing patients in the surgical clinic. In Internal Medicine and Pediatrics, scrubs are usually worn only when you are on call. During your obstetrics/gynecology rotation, scrubs are the norm, especially when you are delivering babies or planning to go to the OR.

Do I need to wear a white coat?

> Although many rotations do not require you to wear a white coat, most students do so because it is simply easier to carry your equipment in your coat pockets. During your psychiatry or pediatric rotation, the attending physician may prefer that team members not wear a white coat. It should go without saying but since I've seen this happen many times, I'll emphasize one other point here. Do not wear clothes, scrubs, or white coats that are dirty or stained with blood or other bodily fluids.

Mistake # <u>27</u>

Eating during rounds

Eating during attending rounds is frowned upon by many attending physicians. This also holds true for chewing gum. So unless your attending unequivocally states that eating during rounds is acceptable, don't do it. This also holds true for drinks. A pet peeve of many attending physicians is bringing in coffee or other beverages into a patient's hospital room.

Part V

Commonly Made Mistakes

With Residents and Interns

In most, if not all, of your rotations, you will be part of a team. As a third year medical student, you will be the most junior member of this team. Above you on this totem pole are the intern, resident, and attending physician. You will be spending most of your time with the intern and resident. Since both often have significant input into the determination of your grade, it is in your best interests to develop a solid working relationship with these individuals. In fact, rotation success often hinges on the relationship that you build with these team members.

Building solid relationships with these individuals requires some knowledge about their roles on the team. Every patient on the team is assigned to an intern, who functions as the patient's primary caregiver. When issues arise during the patient's hospitalization, it is the intern who is often the first to be notified by the nurse or other healthcare professionals. Interns work hard to make sure the things that need to be done for their patients get done. Among other activities, they order lab tests, write progress notes, call consultants, write orders, and even draw blood. Interns work hard to provide the best possible care for their patients.

Interns often turn to their resident for advice. Residents supervise interns, providing them with guidance in matters that they are not yet comfortable with. The resident is essentially the leader of the team. As the leader of the team, the resident is responsible for conducting morning rounds. During rounds, the interns and medical students inform the resident about what has happened to the patient since the previous day's rounds. The resident then helps make decisions as to what needs to be done for the patient on that particular day. It is the resident's responsibility to make sure that the interns and medical students carry out these activities.

As you can see, residents and interns are busy people with many demands placed upon them. As a medical student, you can make their lives easier in so many ways. The best way to do this is to take on as much responsibility for your patients as you can. Essentially, you should strive to function as your patient's intern. By being a productive team member that enhances team efficiency, you will go a long way in impressing the resident and intern. In this chapter, we will discuss mistakes students make with residents and interns.

Mistake # <u>28</u>

Not making a to-do list

On the hospital wards things can move at dizzying speeds. During rounds your resident may ask you to take care of a number of things. It's in your best interests to write everything down. As you complete each task, you can cross it off your list. Don't try to memorize the tasks that need to be completed—that's a recipe for disaster. You may not be lauded for getting everything done, but your resident or intern will be more disappointed and upset if you forget to do something.

Success tip # 12

On a daily basis, your resident may assign you patient-care tasks. Make sure you write these down. Don't rely on your memory because if you forget to do something, your resident will have to answer to the attending.

Mistake # <u>29</u>

Not prioritizing the tasks that need to be completed

After seeing your patients every morning, the team will decide upon a plan of action for that day. This plan may involve a variety of tasks, including laboratory testing, performing studies, and requesting consultations. Some of these tasks are clearly more important than the others. The importance of each of these tasks is something that you will have to ascertain from talking with your resident and intern. Tasks that are of higher priority should be tackled first. In addition, some tasks will not be done that day unless you tackle them early. For example, if you don't call consults and order diagnostic testing early in the day, they are not likely to be done until the following day.

Mistake # <u>30</u>

Not being easily accessible

Patients admitted to the hospital often have complex problems. Their status can change quickly, necessitating decisions regarding diagnosis and management. Your resident and intern would like to have you involved as much as possible in patient care. To keep you involved, you need to be easily accessible. Your busy resident and intern only have a short time to reach you before they take care of the matter on their own.

To remain easily accessible to the resident and intern, you should carry a beeper. In most cases, your hospital or medical school will provide you with a beeper. If you are not given one, you should consider getting one.

If you do not have a beeper, you will have to limit yourself to one particular area (i.e., team's conference room). That way, when the resident or intern needs to get a hold of you, they know where to find you.

Mistake # <u>31</u>

Calling it a day before it's okay

After finishing your work for the day, always touch base with your intern or resident before leaving the hospital or clinic. This ensures that everyone is on the same page and that patient care tasks for the day have actually been completed. Also, always ask the resident if there is anything you can help out with. If the resident or intern says that it is okay to leave, then go ahead and call it a day.

Success tip # 13

NEVER leave for the day without touching base with your resident. Ask him or her if there's anything you can do to help. If he or she says it's okay to take off, go ahead and leave.

Mistake # <u>32</u>

Not eliciting feedback from the resident and intern

One of the most common complaints medical students have about their rotation experience is the lack of feedback. Eliciting feedback from your intern and resident is crucial. After all, you need to know what you are doing well and what you need to work on. In a perfect world, each of your team members would sit down with you periodically to give you feedback on your performance. In reality, this rarely happens unless you are proactive in seeking feedback.

Formal one-on-one feedback sessions should definitely take place halfway through the rotation. At this point in the rotation, you should meet with the resident and intern. This meeting will give you a good feel for how you are doing. Be sure to ask each of your superiors about the things you are doing well (keep doing these things!) and the areas you need to improve upon. You can then focus your efforts on turning your weaknesses into strengths during the remainder of the rotation. If your superiors do not initiate this meeting, make sure you do so. I can't begin to tell you how important this mid-rotation meeting is.

Success tip # 14

In a perfect world, your intern and resident would meet with you halfway through the rotation to discuss your performance. This often does not happen. So if it doesn't, initiate this meeting yourself. If you don't have this meeting, you won't know what you are doing well and what you need to work on. You can then turn your weaknesses into strengths.

Mistake # <u>33</u>

Not volunteering for procedures

If the resident or intern asks if you are interested in doing a procedure, you should enthusiastically say, "Yes!" This is an opportunity for you to display your motivation to learn. Residents love medical students who are motivated.

Mistake # <u>34</u>

Not being a team player

Taking care of patients well requires a team effort. Everyone on the team must carry his or her weight. Only then will things run smoothly. You should be enthusiastic in your efforts to provide assistance in the care of your patients. In addition, you should be receptive to helping out with any patient. If you do not do your part, you will not be perceived as a team player. Very few things irritate residents and interns more than a medical student who is not a team player.

If you don't establish good rapport with your resident and intern, it may come back to haunt you in a number of ways. First, your resident and intern will be less likely to spend the time needed to make sure you have a firm grasp on your patients' problems. Quite often, residents and interns can help medical students predict the questions the attending may ask during attending rounds. Second, recall that your resident and, sometimes your intern, will have a say in the determination of your overall grade. Third, remember that the various team members may talk about your performance. I routinely ask my resident and intern about their thoughts regarding a medical student's performance before I complete my evaluation. That's because the resident and intern spend more time with the students than I do. I want to make sure that the picture that I have formed in my mind is congruent with their thoughts.

Success tip # 15
Being a team player is the KEY to securing a great evaluation from your resident.

Mistake # 35

Making the resident or intern look bad in front of the attending

During attending rounds, there may be times when the attending physician poses questions to the interns and residents, questions to which they do not know the answer but that you do. You may be surprised to learn that you know things that your residents don't, but keep in mind that you will often have much more time to read about your patient's problems than they will. In addition, basic science questions often come up during attending rounds that you will feel more comfortable answering by virtue of the fact that you are closer to the basic science years of medical school.

Nevertheless, if your attending physician asks an intern or resident a question that you know the answer to but they don't, no matter how much you want to, refrain from answering the question. Blurting out the answer to a question not directed to you is considered bad form—your residents may feel that you are showing them up. Remember that you want to maintain a solid relationship with them.

If, however, the attending physician turns to you and asks you the same question, then feel free to answer the question. If you know the answer, try to answer the question with some humility ("I was just reading about this yesterday and...").

Mistake # <u>**36**</u>

Refusing to do scut

Interns often have to complete tasks referred to as "scut" on a daily basis. This term refers to tasks which may or may not be directly related to patient care and that are often the responsibility of other health care professionals. Examples include obtaining supplies and going to the laboratory with specimens or paperwork.

While interns will do most of this work, don't be surprised if your resident asks you to help out with scutwork. They may ask you to draw blood on a patient that you are not following or to order pizza for the team for dinner on an admit day. When you are asked to do scutwork, accept it with a smile. All the team members have to do some degree of scut. Helping your intern out with these tasks and activities will show that you are a team player.

Mistake # <u>**37**</u>

Telling lies

Whatever you do, don't lie. If you make a mistake or forget to do something, own up to it. Remember that everyone makes mistakes. And everyone forgets to do something from time to time. Be honest, because if you are not and you are caught, patient care could be compromised. In addition, there will be serious consequences in terms of the rest of your rotation experience and your overall evaluation.

Part VI

Commonly Made Mistakes

During Attending Rounds

The attending physician is the most senior member of the team. His or her primary goal is to make sure that the patients assigned to the team receive the best possible care. Coming in a close second to this primary goal is providing a solid educational experience for the resident, interns, and medical students.

Your interaction with the attending physician will often be limited to attending rounds. During these rounds the entire team will meet. What happens during attending rounds will vary from day to day. If the team admitted new patients on the previous day, the attending physician will expect formal patient presentations on these patients. These oral presentations are usually given either by medical students or interns.

If new patients were not admitted on the previous day, attending rounds may consist of the team members providing updates on the patients. At other times the attending physician may give a talk or ask other team members to give talks.

Since the attending physician has considerable input into the determination of your overall grade, one of your goals should be to impress him or her in a positive way. You can do this by being well read on your patients' problems, delivering solid oral patient presentations, giving terrific talks, and turning in thoughtful and thorough patient write-ups. In this chapter, we will discuss mistakes made by medical students during attending rounds. The mistakes that are made during oral patient presentations, patient write-ups, and talks will be discussed in subsequent chapters.

Mistake # <u>**38**</u>

Being late for attending rounds

Attending physicians are busy folks. They have often blocked out at least several hours of their day to teach you. That doesn't mean that they have let go of their other responsibilities—rather, they have adjusted their schedule to accommodate the needs of the team.

Success tip # 16
ALWAYS arrive early for attending rounds. While being early or on time certainly doesn't guarantee honors, being late will negatively affect your evaluation.

If your attending physician says that rounds will begin at 10:15 every morning, it behooves you to be ready to go at 10:15. Not 10:20 or 10:25 but 10:15. This may seem obvious to you, and yet students repeat this mistake time and time again.

There may be times, however, when a patient problem arises that prevents you from being on time (i.e., Mr. Smith develops chest pain at 10:10). In these cases, patient care obviously takes precedence. Your attending will certainly understand this.

Mistake # <u>39</u>

Lack of enthusiasm

Because medical students do not have the experience that interns and residents have, they are not expected to perform at an intern or resident level. However, one area in which they can outshine the housestaff is in exhibiting enthusiasm. Attending physicians are impressed with enthusiastic students, especially those who show a passion for learning.

Mistake # <u>40</u>

Not eliciting feedback from the attending physician

One of the most common complaints medical students have about their rotation experience is the lack of feedback. Eliciting feedback from your attending physician is crucial to the learning process. Many students assume that they are performing well if they don't hear otherwise, but this assumption can be misleading. Not uncommonly, students who do not receive feedback during the rotation are surprised when they receive a poor evaluation. These students usually have no idea that they were performing poorly or not meeting the expectations of their attending. Herein lies the importance of eliciting feedback from the attending physician. In a perfect world, the attending physician would sit down with you periodically to give you feedback on your performance. In reality, this rarely happens unless you are proactive in seeking feedback.

A formal one-on-one feedback session should take place halfway through the rotation. This meeting will give you a good feel for how you are doing. Be sure to ask the attending physician about the things you are doing well (keep doing these things!) and the areas where you need to improve. You can then focus your efforts on turning your weaknesses into strengths during the remainder of the rotation. If your attending physician does not initiate this meeting with you, make sure you bring it up. I can't begin to tell you important this mid-rotation meeting is.

Success tip # 17

In a perfect world, your attending physician would meet with you halfway through the rotation to discuss your performance. I can tell you that this often does not happen. So if it doesn't, initiate this meeting yourself. If you don't have this meeting, you won't know what you are doing well and what you need to work on. Once you know what you need to work on, you can turn these weaknesses into strengths, thereby earning a better evaluation.

Feedback can be positive or negative. Before responding to negative feedback, it's a good idea to summarize what your superior has told you to make sure that you clearly understand it. Regardless of whether you agree with the criticism, do not respond emotionally. Things are likely to get worse with an emotional response. Instead, carefully choose your words without sounding defensive, always keeping control over your tone of voice and body language. If you made a major mistake, admit that you are at fault without making excuses, apologize, and inform your attending that you will improve. Remember to always thank your attending for giving you feedback.

Mistake # __41__

Not giving the attending physician your undivided attention

As mentioned earlier, your attending physician is interested in teaching you and has blocked out time from his or her schedule to do so. This block of time the attending physician will spend with the team is called attending rounds. So when the attending physician is with the team, give the attending physician your full attention. This may seem like common sense but you would be surprised how often I have seen medical students make this type of mistake. Here are some examples:

- Eating during rounds

- Writing or typing progress notes during rounds

- Working on the computer during rounds

- Falling asleep during rounds

Success tip # 18
The attending physician should be the focus of your attention during attending rounds. Do whatever you can to avoid looking bored or falling asleep during rounds.

If your attending physician should come back to the conference room after rounds to discuss some issue, pay attention. If you return back to your conference room to find your attending physician there, join the discussion that is taking place. Show your attending physician that what he or she says is important to you.

Mistake # **42**

Not knowing how to present patients

On post-call days (the day that follows a day in which your
team admitted new patients), you will formally present your
newly admitted patient(s) to the attending physician. The
duration of this oral patient presentation varies depending
upon the preference of the attending (as well as the
rotation) but is typically 5 to 10 minutes long. This
presentation helps the attending get a good feel for what is
going on with the patient. A solid presentation allows the
attending physician to formulate a diagnostic and
therapeutic plan. One of the keys to impressing your
attending physician is to deliver outstanding oral patient
presentations. We discuss oral patient presentations in a
subsequent chapter.

Mistake # **43**

Not being well read on your patient's problems

Most of the questions that you will be asked during
attending rounds will deal with issues specific to your
patients. To field these questions appropriately, you need to
be well read on your patient's problems. This involves
reading as much as possible.

Too often, medical students rely only on handbooks to take
care of their patients and field questions from attending
physicians. While handbooks should certainly be one of
your resources, it behooves you to read about your
patients' problems in larger, more authoritative texts.
Handbooks are a distillation of information, often directed at

46

students or interns. Your attending physician will have a deeper knowledge of the various problems and will often ask questions that are not easily answered by reliance on handbooks alone.

Success tip # 19

READ. READ. READ. I can't emphasize this enough. To really impress your attending physician, you need to have a strong grasp on your patients' problems. You can't do this by relying solely on handbooks.

Another common mistake medical students make has to do with not being knowledgeable about the patient's other medical problems. For example, a patient may come in with asthma exacerbation. In his past medical history, the patient may have a history of diabetes mellitus. What often happens with such a patient is that the student becomes well read about asthma exacerbation but doesn't spend much time reading about diabetes. When the patient is placed on corticosteroids for treatment of the asthma, the blood sugar increases markedly. The student is then at a loss in terms of treatment because he or she didn't read up on the management of diabetes. To avoid this problem, it is important to be well read on not only the primary problem (the one that brought the patient to the hospital) but also the other problems. That way, when things change in your patient's hospital course, you will be ready to handle them.

Mistake # **44**

Feeling like you should have the answers to every question

Attending physicians like to get medical students involved as much as possible in the discussion regarding the various patients on the team. One way to do this is to ask them questions. During attending rounds, you are going to be asked a lot of questions, many of which you cannot answer.

You will hopefully be able to answer most of the questions directed your way regarding your own patients. Even being well read on your patients' problems, however, may not provide you with the answers to every possible question your attending physician may ask you about your patient. In addition, questions about other patients may come up that you do not have the answers to. Don't worry. You are not expected to have the answers to all of the questions.

Mistake # <u>45</u>

Not paying attention to patients presented or discussed by other students or interns

During attending rounds, you will hear about patients on the team that you are not following. When other team members are presenting patients, pay close attention to what they are saying. This is not the time to let your mind wander because you never know when the attending may involve you.

When I listen to oral patient presentations, I take notes about each patient. I am then able to sort through things easier. What I recommend to my medical students is that they do the same. That way, if I get them involved in the discussion, they are able to contribute because they have been actively processing the information that is being conveyed to them by the other team members.

If you don't pay attention to patients presented by other team members, you will set yourself up for an uncomfortable and awkward situation should your attending physician ask you for your thoughts.

Mistake # __46__

Leaving attending rounds early to go to conference

On your rotations, you will have regularly scheduled medical student conferences, some of which are mandatory and others optional. It's not unusual for attending rounds to extend past the time that's officially allotted for them. If this happens and you need to get to a conference, it can lead to an awkward situation, in which you will have to get up and make your way to the door. Your attending physician may not appreciate the interruption and may also wonder why going to the conference is more important than staying for rounds.

The easy to way handle this situation is to inform the attending physician about your conference schedule. You can give him or her a copy of the schedule early in the rotation. You can gently remind the attending, preferably before attending rounds, that you have a mandatory conference after rounds so that he or she is not surprised later.

Mistake # __47__

Not asking questions

It's a good idea to ask questions during attending rounds. It shows your interest. If possible, try to formulate these questions the night before attending rounds. A possible way to pose these questions is as follows:

"I was reading about the management of hypertension last night and I realized that there are so many choices available to the physician in terms of antihypertensive therapy. With so many choices, how do you decide which type of antihypertensive agent should be started?"

In this example, note the question started with a comment that the student was reading. This shows that you are, indeed, reading about the patients' problems. Try not to ask questions about purely esoteric topics.

Your goal is to ask pertinent and probing questions regarding the etiology, pathogenesis, diagnosis, and treatment of the disease process. This will demonstrate an attitude of intellectual curiosity, which is clearly an attribute of the honors student.

Mistake # 48

Not appreciating the pet peeves of the attending

You should keep a close watch out for things that irritate the attending physician. You should be able to pick up on most of these things early in the rotation. In the first few days of the rotation, you have a grace period so to speak during which your attending physician won't expect much from you. This is because you are new to the rotation and everyone realizes that you need some time to get comfortable.

During this time, it's best to lay low and observe the things that go on during attending rounds. In particular, pay close attention to other team members who are presenting patients. If your intern is presenting a case and the attending corrects him or her, make a note of it. Do not repeat the same mistake.

Mistake # **49**

Being unfamiliar with your attending physician's background

Most attending physicians have a particular area of interest within their specialty. By doing a little research (i.e., medline search or department website), you can learn about your attending's interests, which are likely to come up at some point during your rotation. Develop a working knowledge of these interests so that you can engage in an intelligent conversation about the subject or field questions.

Let's take an example. Suppose you learn that your attending physician during the Internal Medicine rotation is a gastroenterologist. It would behoove you to read up on high-yield topics in gastroenterology so that when these topics come up (and they almost always do), you can put yourself in a good position to answer questions directed your way. That's not to say that you won't be asked questions outside of gastroenterology. But keep in mind that if your attending physician spends a lot of time in a specialized area, he or she is naturally going to be more passionate and well versed in that area.

Make it a habit to discover your attending's area of expertise and brush up on that area. You won't regret it.

Part VII

Commonly Made Mistakes

When Presenting Newly Admitted Patients

On post-call days (the day following a day during which the team admitted new patients), the attending physician will expect formal oral patient presentations on the newly admitted patients. These oral patient presentations are typically given by the junior members of the team (medical students or interns). If you have been assigned one or more patients, you will be expected to deliver oral patient presentations on the following day during attending rounds. The quality of your oral patient presentations plays a large role in the determination of your overall grade. We will consider common mistakes that medical students make during oral patient presentations on newly admitted patients in this chapter.

Mistake # **50**

Not realizing the type of presentation the attending physician is looking for

The type of presentation expected depends upon whether the patient is newly admitted or not. On post-call days, you will formally present your newly admitted patient to the attending physician. The attending physician expects a complete presentation because he or she is not familiar with the case. The duration of this oral patient presentation varies according to the preference of the attending (as well as the rotation) but is typically 5 to 10 minutes long. This presentation helps the attending get a good feel for what is going on with the patient. A solid presentation allows the attending physician to formulate a diagnostic and therapeutic plan. One of the keys to impressing your attending physician is to deliver outstanding oral patient presentations on newly admitted patients.

This type of presentation differs from the one that you give for previously admitted patients. For these patients, what the attending physician is looking for is a quick update on the patient's hospital course (what has happened since the last time you discussed the patient).

Success tip # 20

One of the reasons it is so important to meet with the attending physician early in the rotation is to find out how he or she wants you to present patients. If you don't do this, be prepared for your attending physician to correct you during rounds.

Mistake # 51

Not rehearsing the oral patient presentation

The oral patient presentation is your chance to impress the attending physician. Delivering an outstanding oral patient presentation requires you to rehearse your presentation multiple times. You cannot expect to do well if you have only practiced your presentation one or two times. In addition to practicing multiple times, try to present the case to your resident and/or intern. They can be invaluable to you in polishing your presentation. If you are able to consistently deliver polished presentations, your attending physician will reward your efforts when he or she sits down to complete your evaluation.

Success tip # 21

Practice makes perfect holds true for oral patient presentations also. One of the biggest mistakes medical students make is not rehearsing enough.

Mistake # <u>52</u>

Oral patient presentation has too little or too much detail

How detailed a presentation should be also varies with the rotation. During your internal medicine and pediatric clerkship, your superiors will expect very detailed presentations. This is in contrast to the surgery clerkship. Surgeons prefer brief and focused presentations.

Before hearing your presentation, your attending physician has a preconceived idea as to the amount of information he or she wants to hear. Your goal is to avoid delivering oral presentations that are too detailed or that are not detailed enough.

How do you know what the attending physician wants? You can learn about the attending's preferences by meeting early in the rotation to discuss their expectations. Once you know exactly what they prefer, you can tailor the oral patient presentations to meet their needs.

Mistake # <u>53</u>

Presentation goes beyond the allotted time

At the beginning of a rotation, you should ask the attending physician how much time you have to give your oral presentation on newly admitted patients. Remember that your attending has a preconceived notion as to how much time your oral patient presentation should take. He or she may not volunteer this information so it's a good idea to ask early in the rotation.

Mistake # <u>54</u>

Patient's chief complaint is not stated in the patient's own words

After providing the attending physician with the patient's name and room number, your oral presentation on newly admitted patients will begin with the chief complaint. When you ask the patient "What brought you into the hospital or clinic today", it is the patient's answer or description of the symptom that is the chief complaint. So if your patient comes in with shortness of breath, don't report that the patient's chief complaint is dyspnea. Although shortness of breath and dyspnea are considered synonymous, the attending physician wants to hear the chief complaint as expressed to you by the patient.

Mistake # <u>55</u>

The history of present illness (HPI) is not presented in chronological order

The HPI is the patient's story regarding the problem that prompted them to seek medical attention. When you present the history of present illness, the information that you convey should flow like a story. After describing the patient's HPI, the attending physician should have a clear idea of the events that transpired before the patient sought medical attention. Very few things irritate attending physicians more than a disjointed HPI, especially one in which the information is not presented chronologically.

Success tip # 22
Make sure your HPI is in chronological order. Very few things irritate attending physicians more than a disjointed HPI, especially one in which the information is not presented chronologically.

Within the HPI, when referring to a day when something happened, it is preferable to use the words "prior to admission" rather than the day itself. For example, it is better to say, "The patient developed chest pain three days prior to admission (PTA)," than "The patient developed chest pain on Wednesday."

Mistake # 56

The first sentence of the HPI does not include the necessary information

Most attending physicians agree that the first sentence of the HPI should include the patient's age, race, and sex. In addition, many attending physicians prefer their medical students include any past medical history (PMH) that relates to what you feel is the underlying problem. An example:

> Example: *"Mrs. Smith is a 64-year old Hispanic female with a PMH significant for coronary artery disease, diabetes mellitus, and hypertension who presents with chest pain."*

Mrs. Smith may also have had a PMH significant for sensorineural hearing loss but since this does not have direct relevance to her chief complaint of chest pain, it is not included in the first line of the HPI.

Mistake # 57

The HPI does not end properly

The HPI should end with the patient presenting to the emergency room, clinic, etc. Often, your last sentence should end with a statement such as—

"...and so he came to the ER for evaluation."

Mistake # <u>58</u>

A complete medication list is not obtained

It is important to obtain the patient's complete medication list. In some cases, doing so is quite easy because the patient will bring in a list of their medications. Remember to always ask about any over-the-counter or herbal medications since patients often don't consider them to be "medications."

You will also encounter patients who have no clue as to what their medications are. They may start by telling you, "I take a green pill and two white pills." In these cases, you may have to call a family member or their pharmacy for the medication information.

Mistake # <u>59</u>

The dosage, route, or frequency of the medications is not known

For some attendings, a simple list of the current medications without any information regarding dosage, route, or frequency of the medications is sufficient. Others expect their medical students to include this information. What you will include will vary with your attending physician's preferences. Irrespective of what your attending physician prefers, you need to have this information readily available in order to provide appropriate patient care.

Mistake # **60**

The inpatient medications are included

A common mistake made by medical students is the reporting of inpatient medications. When presenting a newly admitted patient to your attending physician, you should include only the medications the patient was taking prior to admission (outpatient medications). The medications that you and the team started after the patient was hospitalized (inpatient medications) should not be included here. These will be discussed in your assessment and plan.

Mistake # **61**

Not knowing the reason the patient is taking the medication(s)

Attending physicians expect their students to know why the patient is on a certain medication. Every medication the patient is currently taking should be explained by a medical problem. If it's not easily explained by a medical condition, consider the possibility that the patient failed to inform you about one of their medical conditions or that you failed to elicit the information. In other cases, the patient may have been started on the medication for a particular problem that is no longer active—in these cases, the patient may not need that medication.

Success tip # 23
You should know the reason why your patient is taking each medication. Your attending is likely to ask for this information.

I not only expect the students on my team to have the entire list of medications, including dosages, but I also routinely ask why the patient is on each medication. In talking with other attending physicians, I know I am not alone in this practice.

Mistake # <u>62</u>

Not knowing the patient's allergies

When asked about their allergies, patients may offer information regarding seasonal, environmental, or food allergies. While this information is certainly important and should be documented, what is most important is whether the patient has a history of medication allergies.

If the patient reports that they are allergic to a certain medication, that medication needs to be listed, along with the reaction the patient developed. Many patients believe they are allergic to a certain medication when, in fact, what they experienced was a medication side effect. One of the most common mistakes made is not eliciting the details of the reaction.

Mistake # <u>63</u>

Too much time is spent conveying the review of systems (ROS)

The review of systems is essentially a checklist that should be performed just before the physical examination. The review of systems should be complete. If you are having difficulty constructing a complete ROS, a useful resource is your physical diagnosis book.

When presenting the ROS, however, including everything would make your presentation stretch on and on. Find out in advance what your attending expects to hear in the ROS.

Mistake # <u>64</u>

Too much time is spent conveying the physical exam

Attending physicians expect medical students to perform complete physical examinations. Although residents and interns often perform a more focused exam, it is your responsibility to be thorough and complete. At this point in your career, you are developing your physical examination skills. So even if you think that a funduscopic or rectal exam is not pertinent to your patient's chief complaint, it behooves you to perform these parts of the physical exam.

In terms of the oral presentation, however, your attending may not want to hear the entire physical examination because it takes too much time. Find out what your attending expects when reporting physical exam findings.

Mistake # **65**

No comment is made about the patient's general appearance when reporting the physical exam findings

Within seconds of meeting a patient, the experienced clinician can learn a lot by simply noting the patient's general appearance. Medical students often omit this in their oral patient presentations.

Mistake # **66**

Vital signs are not taken by the medical student

Most attending physicians expect medical students to take the patient's vital signs. They do not feel it is appropriate to merely record the vital signs as documented by the nurse. One reason for this is that attending physicians want to make sure students are comfortable with all facets of the physical examination. In addition, if you report the vital signs taken by the nurse, it doesn't really reflect your encounter with the patient.

Mistake # **67**

Clinical significance of the physical exam findings is not known

If you elicit abnormal physical exam findings, you should know the clinical significance of the abnormalities. The physical examination abnormalities may lend further support to your working diagnosis. For example, if your patient has a history of shortness of breath with exertion, orthopnea, and paroxysmal nocturnal dyspnea (PND), an S3 is an exam finding that lends further support to the diagnosis of congestive heart failure.

At other times, however, you will elicit abnormal findings that have nothing to do with the patient's chief complaint or HPI. In these cases, you should do some research to ascertain the clinical significance of the abnormality and to determine what further evaluation is needed for the finding.

Mistake # 68

Current lab test results are not known

You should convey all of the patient's current laboratory test results to your attending physician during your presentation. This sounds simple enough. But you would be surprised at how often a medical student will tell me "Oh, I didn't write that down."

At other times the student tells me that it's not back yet, only to be followed by the intern giving me the result. As a general rule, you should check for laboratory test results just before attending rounds so that you are completely up-to-date.

Mistake # 69

Previous lab test results are not known

When conveying abnormal lab test results, it is important to also relay previous results. That way the listener has a point of reference. Comparing the current laboratory test abnormality with the previous result often has a major impact upon the diagnosis and management of the patient.

For example, if the patient has an elevated serum creatinine level, you should include the previous serum creatinine. This will help your listener determine if the patient has acute or chronic renal failure and what further work-up, if any, is needed.

Mistake # **70**

Not knowing what the abnormal lab test results mean

Many of the patients assigned to you will have abnormal lab test results. In some cases, the etiology is apparent. You should always ask yourself if the laboratory test abnormality supports or refutes your working diagnosis.

In many cases, however, the etiology is not clear. It is your job to not only identify the potential causes but also to determine the most likely explanation for the abnormality.

Success tip # 24
If your patient has abnormal lab test results, your attending will ask you about them. Be ready to field these questions.

Attending physicians love to ask medical students about the clinical significance of abnormal lab tests. If you are not sure why the lab test is abnormal, at a minimum, you should have a differential diagnosis for the abnormality (the major or common causes but not a list of 50 things). The attending physician will be more impressed, though, if you can explain which one of the entities in the differential diagnosis is the likely etiology and what further work-up is needed.

Mistake # 71

The EKG is not brought to attending rounds

As a general rule, if you obtain an EKG on your patient, you should bring it with you to attending rounds. The attending physician expects to review it during rounds, often while you are giving your thoughts regarding the findings.

Mistake # 72

Not knowing how to interpret the EKG

An EKG is ordered on many patients who are hospitalized. As with any other study, you should know how to interpret it. For medical students, EKG interpretation can be quite challenging. Even though you have been introduced to EKGs during your basic science years, you have not been in the habit of interpreting them on a regular basis.

At some point during your third year of medical school, you will probably have lectures on EKG interpretation, usually during your Internal Medicine rotation. Hopefully, these lectures are given early in the rotation. But if the EKG lectures are spaced out throughout the rotation, you will not have the knowledge you need to interpret EKGs at a time when you need it the most—that is, when the attending physician asks you to interpret an EKG during rounds.

Early in the rotation, attending physicians do not expect yo to be adept at EKG interpretation since you lack experience. But as the rotation progresses their expectations will increase.

The key to EKG interpretation is to develop a system that you use for every EKG you encounter. By sticking to this system, you will ensure that you do not miss any important findings. You should consider asking your resident or intern to introduce you to their system. Most housestaff adhere to a particular system.

Please refer to the website, http://www.MD2B.net, to view our system for EKG interpretation.

Success tip # 25
Always be ready to discuss the patient's EKG findings during attending rounds.

Mistake # 73

Not reviewing the EKG with the resident or intern

Attending physicians love to ask their medical students to interpret EKGs. So if an EKG is obtained on your patient, it is in your best interests to review it with the intern or resident. Because they have had more experience with reading EKGs, your intern or resident will be able to point out the significant findings. Even if you feel comfortable reading EKGs, it is still worthwhile to do this to make sure your interpretation is correct.

'4

Medical student's EKG interpretation is not their own

Attending physicians do not expect students to be masters of EKG interpretation. After all, this is not an area of emphasis during the first two years of medical school. Because of inexperience in this area, attending physicians realize that medical students will go over the EKG with the housestaff and fully expect them to do so.

When you report the EKG findings, keep in mind that it is reasonable for him or her to ask you about your findings. For example, if you report left ventricular hypertrophy, then make sure that you are familiar with the criteria for left ventricular hypertrophy. If you don't know the criteria, your attending will realize that you are simply repeating what someone else told you. I have also seen students relay the machine interpretation of the EKG, which is often included in the EKG printout.

Mistake # 75

The chest x-ray is not brought to attending rounds

As a general rule, if you obtain a chest x-ray on your patient, you should bring it with you to attending rounds. The attending physician expects to review it during rounds, usually while you are giving your thoughts regarding the findings.

Mistake # <u>76</u>

Not knowing how to interpret the chest x-ray

A chest x-ray is ordered on many patients who are hospitalized. As with any other study, you should know how to interpret it. For medical students, the interpretation of the chest x-ray can be quite challenging. Even though you have been introduced to the chest x-ray during your basic science years, you have not been in the habit of interpreting them on a regular basis.

At some point during your third year of medical school, you will probably have lectures on chest x-ray interpretation, usually during your Internal Medicine rotation. Hopefully, these lectures are given early in the rotation. But if the chest x-ray lectures are spaced throughout the rotation, you will not have the knowledge you need to interpret chest x-rays at a time when you need it the most—that is, when the attending physician asks you to interpret a chest x-ray during rounds.

Early in the rotation, attending physicians do not expect you to be adept at chest x-ray interpretation since you lack experience in this area. But as the rotation progresses, their expectations will increase.

The key to chest x-ray interpretation is to develop a system that you use for every chest x-ray you encounter. By sticking to this system, you will ensure that you do not miss any important findings. You should consider asking your resident or intern to introduce you to their system—most housestaff adhere to a particular system.

Please refer to the website, http://www.MD2B.net, to view our system for chest x-ray interpretation.

Success tip # 26
Always be ready to describe the chest x-ray findings during attending rounds.

Mistake # **77**

Not reviewing the chest x-ray with the resident or intern

Attending physicians love to ask their medical students to interpret chest x-rays. So if a chest x-ray is obtained on your patient, review it with the intern or resident. Chances are good that your attending physician will ask for your thoughts regarding the chest x-ray when you present the case during attending rounds. Because they have had more experience with reading chest x-rays, your intern or resident will be able to point out the significant findings. Even if you feel comfortable reading chest x-rays, it is still worthwhile to go over the chest x-ray with the intern or resident to make sure your interpretation is correct.

Mistake # **78**

Not reviewing the chest x-ray or other imaging test with the radiologist

In addition to reviewing the chest x-ray or other imaging study with the housestaff, you should make it a habit of going over the study with the radiologist. This is because your intern and/or resident may also feel uncomfortable with interpretation of imaging tests. While your housestaff may be able to point out certain findings, there are other findings that they may not appreciate because of inexperience.

I recommend that you review any imaging test you obtain on your patients with the radiologist. When going over the study with the radiologist, offer him or her your own interpretation and then ask the radiologist to comment on your interpretation. By doing so, you will feel much more comfortable when your attending physician asks you to interpret the study during attending rounds.

Reviewing the chest x-ray or other imaging test with the radiologist is not always possible. For example, if your patient is admitted during the night and an imaging test is obtained, you may not have access to a radiologist. In these cases, at least review the study with the housestaff prior to attending rounds.

Mistake # <u>79</u>

No assessment is made

When presenting the assessment and plan, one of the most common errors I have seen is the omission of the assessment. Remember that most of your patients will have multiple problems in their problem list. Each problem should have an assessment even if the problem has nothing to do with why the patient was admitted—the caveat to this rule is in the surgery and obstetrics/gynecology clerkship in which your superiors may not want an extensive problem list. In these rotations, you should include only the active problems.

> Example: *1. Unstable angina. Because this patient, who has a history of coronary artery disease, is now having an increase in the frequency and severity of his chest pain, he is admitted for further evaluation and management of unstable angina. Other major and potentially life threatening*

causes of chest pain such as aortic dissection, pulmonary embolism, and pneumothorax are unlikely after consideration of the history, physical exam, EKG, and chest x-ray. The treatment plan for this patient's unstable angina includes. . .

2. Hypertension - Blood pressure is currently in the target range. Continue hydrochlorothiazide.

Success tip # 27
Always have an assessment before the plan.

Mistake # <u>80</u>

The plan is not understood

When conveying the plan for each of your patient's problems, you should have a clear understanding of why you are recommending what you are recommending. Many attending physicians gauge a student's level of understanding by asking the student to explain his or her treatment choices. For example, if the patient has pneumonia and antibiotic X was chosen, attending physicians will typically ask why that antibiotic was selected. If the student is unable to explain the rationale behind the selection of the antibiotic, the attending physician will conclude that the student is merely relaying (without understanding) the plan that was outlined by the intern or resident.

Success tip # 28

Do you know why you and your team are managing the patient the way you are? If you don't know the rationale behind treatment decisions, you are not ready to present your patient to the attending. Make sure you figure it out before attending rounds.

Part VIII

Commonly Made Mistakes

On Write-Ups

In most if not all of your rotations, you will be expected to turn in patient write-ups for review, usually to the attending physician. These write-ups are essentially a detailed account of the patient's clinical presentation. Although the content will vary depending upon the rotation, in general, the write-up will include the chief complaint, past medical/surgical history, medication list, allergies, social history, family history, review of systems, physical exam, laboratory test results, EKG findings, chest x-ray or other imaging test findings, and the assessment/plan. Except for the assessment and plan, the entire write-up is essentially a presentation of the information you have gathered. What is particularly difficult for most medical students is the assessment and plan. As with your oral patient presentation on newly admitted patients, the quality of your patient write-up plays a large role in the determination of your overall grade. In this chapter, we will discuss the mistakes third year medical students make on patient write-ups.

Mistake # **81**

The write-up is not complete

In most of your rotations, you will be expected to turn in write-ups on patients that you admit into the hospital. In most cases, it is the attending physician who will review these. Write-ups are not to be taken lightly since the quality of the write-ups plays a large role in the determination of your overall grade.

What you include in a write-up varies to some extent with the rotation. At the beginning of the rotation you should find out what you need to include by talking with the attending physician and resident. If you don't have this conversation, you'll see a lot of red marks on your write-ups when they are returned to you.

Mistake # **82**

The chief complaint is not expressed in the patient's own words

History taking begins with elicitation of the patient's chief complaint. When you ask the patient, "What brought you into the hospital or clinic today?" it is the patient's answer or description of the symptom that is the chief complaint. So if your patient comes in with shortness of breath, don't write that the patient's chief complaint is dyspnea. Although shortness of breath and dyspnea are considered synonymous, the attending physician wants you to list the chief complaint as expressed to you by the patient.

Mistake # **83**

The history of present illness (HPI) is not presented chronologically

The HPI is the patient's story regarding the problem that prompted them to seek medical attention. When you present the history of present illness, the information that you convey should flow like a story. After describing the patient's history of present illness, the attending physician should have a clear idea of the events that transpired before the patient sought medical attention. Very few things irritate attending physicians more than a disjointed HPI, especially one in which the information is not presented chronologically.

Mistake # <u>84</u>

The first sentence of the HPI does not include the necessary information

Most attending physicians agree that the first sentence of the HPI should include the patient's age, race, and sex. In addition, many attending physicians prefer that their medical students include any past medical history (PMH) that relates to what you feel is the underlying problem. An example:

> *Example:* *"Mrs. Smith is a 64-year-old Hispanic female with a PMH significant for coronary artery disease, diabetes mellitus, and hypertension who presents with chest pain."*

Mrs. Smith may also have had a PMH significant for sensorineural hearing loss but since this does not have direct relevance to her chief complaint of chest pain, it is not included in the first line of the HPI.

Mistake # <u>85</u>

The last sentence of the HPI is not worded properly

The HPI should end with the patient presenting to the emergency room, clinic, etc. Your last sentence should often end with:

> *Example:* *"...and so he came to the ER for evaluation."*

Mistake # **86**

The past medical history (PMH) is not complete

The past medical history is really a list of the patient's problems. If the problems are related to the chief complaint, they should also be included in the first line of the HPI (see mistake # 84). For each condition in the PMH, you should include the following information:

- How long has he or she had the problem?

- How was the problem diagnosed?

- What diagnostic studies (including lab tests, radiology results, stress tests, pulmonary function tests, etc.) have been done? And if they have been done, what are the results?

Examples: *Hyperlipidemia: dx'd 1999, on simvastatin since then, reportedly with good control. Last lipids(7/00): Total chol—155, LDL—95, HDL –30, Trig 150*

Coronary artery disease: dx'd 1997, by exercise stress test. Exercised to 8'30", 9 mets, stopped secondary to chest pain and 1 mm ST-segment depression. Has been treated with meds since then.

Mistake # <u>87</u>

The medication list does not include over-the-counter and herbal medications

Under the heading, "medications," you should list all of the medications the patient is taking at the time of admission (outpatient medications), including over-the-counter and herbal medications. If the patient is not taking over-the-counter or herbal medications, you should state this. This is not the place to include medications started since admission (inpatient medications).

Next to each medication, you should list the dosage, route, and frequency of the medication. If the patient has been prescribed a medication but is not taking it, it is appropriate to list the medication here followed by the statement not taking in parentheses.

> Examples: *Enteric-coated aspirin 325 mg po qd*
> *Metoprolol 50 mg po bid (not taking).*

Mistake # <u>88</u>

Medical student does not describe the patient's allergies

Under the heading, "allergies," you should list all of the patient's medication allergies. The type of allergic reaction is often omitted but is of major importance. In many cases what a patient considers an allergic reaction to a medication is actually a side effect of the medication (i.e., nausea with codeine).

Examples: Codeine—itching

Penicillin—rash and low blood pressure

Mistake # 89

The review of systems (ROS) is not thorough

The review of systems is essentially a checklist that should be performed just before the physical examination. The review of systems should be complete. If you are having difficulty constructing a complete ROS, a useful resource is your physical diagnosis book.

Mistake # 90

The physical examination is not complete

Attending physicians expect medical students to perform complete physical examinations. Although residents and interns often perform a more focused exam, it is your responsibility to be thorough and complete. This is because you are developing your physical examination skills at this point in your career. So even if you think that a funduscopic or rectal exam is not pertinent to your patient's chief complaint, it behooves you to perform these parts of the physical exam.

Mistake # **91**

There is no assessment before the plan

The assessment should start with a short summary of no more than 3-4 sentences. This summary should be a recapitulation of the important aspects of the patient's clinical presentation. In your final sentence, you should state your diagnosis—or the presumed diagnosis if the diagnosis is not secure.

After the brief summary, you should list all of the patient's problems numerically, with the most important problem first. After each problem, there should be an assessment. How detailed this assessment should be will vary depending on the problem. For the patient's primary problem, you need to explain what the diagnosis is and why you think that particular condition accounts for your patient's clinical presentation. In addition, you need to comment on why other possible diagnoses are unlikely.

For other problems that are not as important, the assessment can be as brief as one line. For example, if the patient came in with COPD exacerbation but also has a history of hypertension, the primary problem is COPD exacerbation and the secondary problem is hypertension. For hypertension, the assessment can be as simple as the following:

1)   *COPD -*

2)   *Hypertension—Patient is currently normotensive. Will continue his current antihypertensive regimen of hydrochlorothiazide and lisinopril.*

Mistake # 92

The write-up is not turned in on time

As mentioned before, in most of your rotations, you will be required to turn in patient write-ups, usually to the attending physician. Be sure to turn in these write-ups on time. Typically, it is the clerkship director or attending physician who will inform you as to when the write-up should be turned in.

Success tip # 29
Always turn in your patient write-ups on time.

Mistake # 93

Suggestions made by the attending physician for future write-ups are not followed

When you get your write-up back, you will see that your attending physician has made comments on it. There will be positive comments on aspects you did particularly well on. There will also be areas, which will need improvement. Pay particular attention to areas that need work, because on your next write-up, you want to avoid these mistakes. By doing so, you are demonstrating improvement.

Success tip # 30
Pay close attention to the comments made on your write-ups. Make sure that you avoid making these same mistakes on future write-ups.

Part IX

Commonly Made Mistakes

When Giving a Talk

Quite often, medical students are asked to give one or more talks, often pertaining to an issue that arises during rounds. Many medical students are overcome with a sense of dread when a talk is assigned to them. I remember feeling the same way when I was assigned talks. "Here's one more thing on my plate and my plate's already full." What I didn't realize then and what many students don't realize today is that a talk is your chance to really impress your team. While you can't control what your attending physician asks you during attending rounds, you do have complete control over your talk. So with the proper amount of preparation and practice, you should be able to deliver a terrific talk. Your team will be impressed with the command you have over this topic. In this chapter we look at the mistakes third year medical students make when giving a talk.

Mistake # <u>94</u>

Not volunteering for a talk

It is not uncommon for the attending physician to assign a talk directly to the medical students. At times, however, the attending physician may turn to the entire team and ask "Who would like to give us a talk about asthma exacerbation?" If such a situation arises, you should be the first person to raise your hand. This is yet another opportunity to demonstrate your enthusiasm, even if you can't stand the idea of preparing and giving a talk.

Most students are not excited about giving talks. In fact, most dread the idea. But look at it this way. Here's a chance for you to shine. You have the stage—the team is your audience. In contrast to attending rounds where the attending physician can ask you just about anything (and you can't possibly prepare for every possible question), you will have a lot of time to prepare for your talk. You can't beat that! Relish this opportunity to perform in front of the team because an outstanding talk can go a long way in impressing your attending.

Mistake # <u>95</u>

Not knowing what you are speaking about

This sounds simple enough. But you'd be surprised how often the content of a student's talk is not the intended subject. Before you begin preparing a talk, make sure you are absolutely certain of the topic. Other questions to ask before preparing your talk:

- How long would you like me to speak?

- When would you like me to give the talk?

- Where will I be giving the talk?

In most cases, your attending physician will assign you a topic. Usually this topic will be broad. For example, your topic may be lung cancer. It's hard to do justice to such a topic unless you have been given a lot of time. So if you have a short amount of time but a broad topic, ask the attending if there is a specific aspect of lung cancer he or she would like you to focus on. If the attending leaves it up to you, pick an aspect of the topic that would be relevant to your audience.

When deciding what to speak about, consider answers to the following questions:

- What does your audience expect?

- What can you cover in the amount of time you have been given?

Mistake # 96

Not knowing when you are expected to give the talk

Make sure you know when the attending physician expects you to give your talk. Consider the following example:

Dr. Jones assigned the topics of thrombocytosis and asthma to his medical students, Paul and George, respectively. He didn't tell them when they would give the talks and neither student asked. Two days later, in the middle of rounds, Dr. Jones said "Since we have a lull in the action, why don't we use this time for student presentations?"

Paul had assumed that he would have longer than a few days to prepare the talk. "Can I give my talk tomorrow? I just need a little more time to work on it."

"Since we have some time, I can go ahead and give my asthma presentation," said George.

George wasn't trying to make Paul look bad. He just had the talk prepared sooner. However, it certainly reflected poorly on Paul. This situation could have been avoided if both students had asked the attending when they should give the talk.

In other cases, you may be ready to give the talk on the date specified by the attending but, for a variety of reasons, you don't get a chance to do so. Usually what happens is that some patient emergency or problem prevents you from giving your talk, and the next day you are on call, and so on. Days pass by and you haven't had a chance to give your talk. Although you would like to get it out of the way, there's not much you can do except be ready to give it on a moment's notice.

Mistake # <u>97</u>

Not using the appropriate resources to prepare your talk

Before you even organize your presentation, you must first select the material for your presentation. The real trick is determining what not to use. Your research is always going to yield more material than you have time to talk about. And, of course, you want to avoid information overload, because there is a limit to what your audience can handle.

Although you may have a number of resources at your disposal to choose the content of your talk, it's best not to rely on handbooks. You should instead turn towards textbooks and recent literature. After all, while the information in your handbooks may suffice for your fellow students, keep in mind that the members of your audience have different levels of training. Be sure you think of this when preparing your talk.

Mistake # **98**

Forgetting to announce your topic

Just because you have been assigned a topic doesn't mean that you shouldn't announce your topic. This is obviously a good way to start any talk and can be as simple as the following:

Today, I will be talking to you about—

It's also a good idea to let your audience know about your subtopics. For example, if your topic is lung cancer, perhaps you will be talking about the subtopics of symptoms, signs, radiology, laboratory tests, etc.

Mistake # **99**

Forgetting what to say

If you ask anyone who has given or is about to give a talk what their biggest fear is, most will tell you they fear going completely blank. Although this is a very real concern for many people, you can, fortunately, take measures to avoid this from happening to you.

This scenario is more likely to happen if you memorize your material. I strongly discourage you from memorizing your entire talk because, more often than not, you will become focused on the words that you want to say rather than the ideas behind the words. In addition, you will lose your ability to engage the audience.

The flip side is reading your entire talk word for word. I strongly discourage this as well. If you read word for word, it's difficult to make eye contact. In addition, you lose normal inflection.

Better alternatives to memorization or reading verbatim are the use of notes or visual aids. If you choose to use notes, I recommend using note cards. The key is to make sure you don't put too much on them. It's also a good idea to set your note cards on a table and move away from them every so often. This will prevent you from relying on them too heavily at the expense of losing your audience.

Visual aids (transparencies, slides, flip charts, blackboards/whiteboards, computer presentations, handouts) are particularly useful because, if done well, they allow you to move from one idea to another by simply moving to the next visual aid (i.e., one slide to another).

Mistake # <u>100</u>

Not projecting energy during the talk

Good speakers project energy when they give a talk. Through their posture, facial expressions, movement, and voice, they come across as being passionate about what they are conveying to you. You should strive to do the same with your talks. You want your audience to realize that you really care about what you are saying. You can achieve this goal by making eye contact with the various members of your audience, speaking at a reasonably quick pace, pausing at appropriate times to emphasize certain points, and minimizing "uhs" during your talk. And finally, if at all possible, practice your talk in front of others. They will be able to let you know if you are coming across as a dynamic speaker.

Mistake # **101**

Talk is too short or too long

When you rehearse your talk, make sure that your talk is not too short or too long. When assigned a talk, it's always a good idea to ask your attending how much time you have to give your talk. Then as you go about putting your talk together, keep these time constraints in mind.

Remember that during attending rounds, there is often a lot that needs to be done in a short amount of time. For this reason, try not to speak for longer than you have been given. On the other hand, too short a talk may leave the attending physician wondering how much time and effort you expended in preparing for the talk.

REQUEST FOR INFORMATION

If you wish to be placed on a mailing list for information concerning new publications and updates, please fill out the form below and mail to:

MD2B
P.O. Box 300988
Houston, Texas 77230-0988

(PLEASE PRINT)

Name_____

Street Address _____

City _____ State_____ Zip _____

Telephone number (optional) _____

Email _____

Medical School _____

Year of graduation _____

FOR FURTHER INFORMATION CALL (713) 927-6830

Visit us on the World Wide Web at http://www.MD2B.net

What Medical Students Say About Other Books by Samir Desai, MD

Clinician's Guide to Laboratory Medicine 2nd edition, ISBN # 1930598742

This handbook provides a step-by-step approach to laboratory test interpretation.

An excellent resource for medical students and residents. For example, the hyponatremia section is more useful than the one in the Wash manual. As they say on the wards, "Strong work!"—Medical student, Northwestern University

I found the book quite helpful on my medicine rotation. The diagnostic trees are extremely useful and helped with my exam because it was a similar style to the clerkship director's method of teaching.—Medical student, Weill Medical College of Cornell University

Your text is wonderful. I have used it quite extensively on my medicine and surgical rotations. During the last four months of my third year many of my classmates and residents have even asked to borrow it.—Medical student, University of Nevada

In our Medicine Clerkship, the *Clinician's Guide to Lab Medicine* has quickly become one of the two most popular paperback books that our students purchase for our clerkship. They also use it for other clerkships. Our students have praised the algorithms, tables, and ease of pursuit of clinical problems through better understanding of the utilization of tests appropriate to the problem at hand. —Director, Third Year Medicine Clerkship at Oregon Health Sciences University

Clinician's Guide to Diagnosis ISBN # 1930598513

This handbook leads the clinician from symptom to diagnosis through a series of steps.

> This book serves as a worthy guide to a stepwise approach to common diagnoses. The information is presented in a simple to follow manner. It is intended to provide a practical approach to commonly encountered symptoms, a worthy objective that the book meets. The author provides a unique step-by-step approach to the diagnosis of common problems. Tables and flowcharts are very well done. Medical students and house officers are the intended audience but I would also add primary care physicians. As a primary care physician, I am impressed with how easy it is to use this quick reference during a busy schedule.—Assistant Professor, Creighton University Medical School.
>
> It made working up a patient so much easier for me. Not only that, it gave me the answers to my attending physician's questions, which made me look like a star!—Medical Student, Ohio State University Medical School
>
> The tables, boxes, and algorithms are wonderful, making it easy to access key information. You can't beat the step-by-step approach that walks you from the patient's symptom to diagnosis. I wish I had gotten this book at the beginning of my third year of medical school.—Medical Student, Wayne State University School of Medicine

Clinician's Guide to Internal Medicine *ISBN # 159195021X*

This pocket-sized book provides quick access to essential information covering diagnosis, treatment, and management of commonly encountered patient problems in Internal Medicine.

> Read this book if you want to ace attending rounds in Internal Medicine.—Medical student, Indiana University Medical School

> Short, concise, and to-the-point. That's what I liked best about this book. It made me look like a stud during my Internal Medicine rotation.—Medical student, University of Texas-Southwestern Medical School

> As soon as I found this book, I put down my Saint-Francis guide. There's no comparison. Clearly one of the best resources I had during my Internal Medicine rotation.—Medical student, University of Washington Medical School

To read a chapter from these books, visit
http://www.MD2B.net